FOLENS SPELLING

BASIC RULES

BOOK 2

Age 7–9

Glendra Read

Folens
Publishers

CONTENTS

© 1993 Folens Limited, on behalf of the author.

First published 1993 by Folens Limited, Dunstable and Dublin.

Illustrations by Chris Masters.   Cover by Graphic Editions.

ISBN 185276390-6

Folens Limited, Albert House, Apex Business Centre, Boscombe Road, Dunstable, LU5 4RL, England.

INTRODUCTION

This book and the National Curriculum

Spelling is Attainment Target 4 in the National Curriculum for English, and spelling should always be seen and used in the wider context of literacy. The purpose of writing is to commit an idea to paper, whether through necessity (lists/instructions/letters), or desire (poems/stories/plays). Correct spelling enables the writer's 'message' to be transmitted with minimum ambiguity to its intended audience.

Spelling can be taught in a structured, developmental way, though children will learn at different rates, and some will learn with ease while others will experience despairing difficulty. This book aims to support teachers of children aged 7-9 years working through National Curriculum Levels 2-4.

Level 2

2a produce recognisable (though not necessarily always correct) spelling of a range of common words.

2b spell correctly; in the course of their own writing, simple monosyllabic words they use regularly which observe common letter patterns.

2c recognise that spelling has patterns, and begin to apply their knowledge of those patterns in their attempts to spell a wider range of words.

2d show knowledge of the names and order of the letters of the alphabet.

Level 3

3a spell correctly; in the course of their own writing, simple polysyllabic words they use regularly which observe common patterns.

3b recognise and use correctly regular patterns for vowel sound and common letter strings.

3c show a growing awareness of word families and their relationships.

3d in revising and redrafting their writing, begin to check the accuracy of their spelling.

Level 4

4a spell correctly; in the course of their own writing, words which display other main patterns in English spelling.

How the book can help with spelling

This book is the second of three *Basic Rules* books. *Basic Rules* book 1, for 5-7-year-olds, deals with early spelling, and *Basic Rules* book 3, for 9-11-year-olds, deals with more complex spelling.

This book aims to:

1. Give children a multi-sensory strategy for learning a new spelling.

2. Cover many common letter patterns which the 7-9-year-old child needs to learn.

3. Help children spell frequently-used words with confidence.

4. Help children extrapolate from one known word to another.

5. Extend more able pupils.

6. Support less able pupils by offering sheets to revise or reinforce basic spellings.

7. Support teachers in the diagnosis of spelling errors.

The sheets can be used for individual, pair, or group work. They can be used for introducing new concepts and letter strings, or for reinforcing areas already covered. The book employs a flexible structure, so that sheets can be used consecutively or in random order.

Expectations of the child aged 7 years.

The child aged 7 years should have grasped some of the basic essentials of spelling. The child should know the letters of the alphabet and the order in which they come. Children should also know the sounds the letters make, the importance of vowels, and begin to understand the concept of syllables. Alongside this, they should begin to apply their knowledge of letter patterns or strings (e.g. sh, ch, ing, oo, ee) to a wider range of words. The child should understand that there is a **correct** way to spell words, but should also be willing to experiment and have a go at an unknown word.

An easy dictionary should be available to check a spelling or a definition. Children should be presenting their work in a pleasing way, with suitable punctuation marks and appropriate capital letters. The practice of joined-up handwriting should have begun.

Through reading a broad variety of books, vocabulary should be increasing. Children aged 7 years should be taking an interest in how words are constructed, and generalising from one word to another, in the quest to develop their spelling in the wider literary context.

What is in the book

There are 45 sheets in the book. The first 15 sheets are aimed at children working around Level 2, the middle 15 sheets for Level 3, and the final 15 sheets are for those working beyond Level 3. If the sheets in this book are at an inappropriate level for any particular child, sheets from book 1 or book 3 of the series can be tried.

Common letter strings are covered, and the wordsearch sheets aim to teach or reinforce irregularly spelt words (e.g. after, want, because). Other areas covered include vowels and consonants, assimilation, alliteration, alphabetical order, syllables, homophones, prefixes and suffixes.

There are two dictation passages which are especially useful for children with spelling difficulties. There is a brief guide to help teachers diagnose and categorise the errors or miscues, and suggestions on how to take remedial measures. There are two word lists, and in the Appendix there is a book list including dictionaries, reference books, thesauri, spelling schemes and computer programs.

How to teach spelling

Teachers can help children develop the basic skills necessary for spelling by encouraging them to **speak** clearly, **listen** carefully, **look** positively and **write** neatly. All the skills of speaking, listening, looking and writing are combined in the complex and dynamic spelling process.

By the time children are 7 years old, they should know the alphabet names for the letters, and be using the 'simultaneous oral spelling' method to learn a spelling (researched by Bryant and Bradley, see Appendix).

The method is this: children **look** at the word to be spelt, **say** the alphabet names, **cover** the word, and **write** it down. After they have covered the word and if they are unable to remember it, they must look again. Finally they need to **check** the word they have written. Children can be helped by this method whether they have weak auditory memories or weak visual memories.

Some children find it difficult to remember long words at one go. Sometimes it can help to encourage them to remember the word syllable by syllable: e.g. for-got-ten is three chunks to remember, instead of nine letters.

Encouraging children to try out a spelling on a piece of paper can help them make a visual check, and help them work towards the correct spelling of a word.

Encourage them to 'have a go'.

Dictionaries

Asking children to 'look up the spelling' in a dictionary may not be helpful if, for instance, the word begins with a silent letter. Some dictionaries (*A.C.E.* or *Dictionary of Perfect Spelling*, see Appendix) index words according to how they sound, e.g., 'knock' can be found under 'k' **and** under 'n'.

Dictionary skills are vital at their formative, 7-9-year-old stage, and children need to be reminded of five points.

They should:

1. Know the alphabet.

2. Know where a letter will come in the dictionary - at the beginning, middle or end.

3. Know that the words at the top of the page show the first word on the page, and the last word on the page.

4. Know alphabetical order **within** a word (e.g., 'after' comes before 'again').

5. Be able to scan quickly down a page to find the required word.

Children with spelling difficulties

Up to the age of 7 years, children will be happily experimenting with spelling, and testing their hypotheses. Often their spellings will be incorrect. It is less usual for the 7-9-year-old child to **continue** to spell incorrectly. The child who does continue to spell in a bizarre fashion, e.g., 'bes' for 'this', or 'darss' for 'danger', needs specialist help from a learning support teacher, or from the school psychological service.

Diagnostic spelling tests, such as those provided in the *Diagnostic Assessment* books in this series, are helpful to indicate what sort of difficulties the child may have. Categorising errors or miscues can reveal **areas** of difficulty. Steps can then be taken to help the child.

The spelling problems which children present us with often cannot be solved by simple or single solutions: every child's problem is unique, and should be tackled with a positive approach and a structured yet flexible format.

Children may see the world full of random, awkwardly spelt words. We as teachers can guide them through this labyrinth of letters, by helping them enunciate clearly, listen with attention, look with curiosity and intent, write legibly, and become familiar with the structure of the English spelling system. Only then will we have helped them towards using spelling in the context of their own writing.

Name _____ Date _____

Vowels and consonants

There are 26 letters in the alphabet.

a e i o u are **vowels**.

The other letters are **consonants**.
Put a ring around all the **vowels** in the alphabet.

a b c d e f g h i j k l m n o p q r s t u v w x y z

Vowels are important. Every word must have **one vowel or more** in it.

1. Put a ring round all the **vowels** in the 'family' words.

baby

mum   uncle   brother   grandmother   dad

mother   sister   aunt   grandfather   father

Write the 'family' words here. Read the words.

_____

_____

2. Put a ring round all the vowels in the planet names.

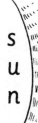     

s   Mercury   Pluto
u   Uranus
n   Earth   Jupiter
        Venus   Mars   Saturn
                                                          Neptune

Write the 'planet' names here. Read the names.

_____

_____

Learn the planet names, in order from the sun.

Blends 1

Sometimes 2 consonants go together.
You can still hear the 2 sounds.

1. Say these sounds to yourself.

br   cr   dr   fr   gr   pr   tr

bl   cl   fl   gl   pl   sl

sm   sn   sp   st   sw

2. Put in the right letters to make each word.

_ _ ar   _ _ an   _ _ ug   _ _ ee

_ _ ide   _ _ ider   _ _ ocks

_ _ og   _ _ am   _ _ y   _ _ ass

_ _ ile   _ _ oss   _ _ oom

_ _ ock   _ _ um   _ _ ass   _ _ ail

3. Choose 6 words. Put each word into a sentence.

1._____

2._____

3._____

4._____

5._____

6._____

Name _____   Date _____

Blends 2

Sometimes 3 consonants go together.
You can still hear the 3 sounds.

spl

scr

spr

str

1. Here are some useful words beginning with these blends. Read them
   Sort the words, and write them in the correct boxes below.

spring   scrub   sprout   splash   street

stream   strap   sprint   splendid   scratch

scrap   screw   string   split   spray

spl	scr	spr	str

2. Find the correct word for the pictures

spr _int_

spl _i t_

scr _ach_

str _ee t_

Antonyms - opposites

Big is the opposite of little.

Big   little

1. Find all the words which are opposites. Write them in pairs on the lines.
   The first one is done for you. Cross the words off as you go along.

Learn to spell like this:

Look   Say   Cover   Write   Check

~~up~~   fast   light   right   new

top   low   left   under   over   cold

high   slow   thin   after   before   ~~down~~   dark

back   front   old   bottom   fat   hot

up _____   down _____   _____   _____

_____   _____   _____   _____

_____   _____   _____   _____

_____   _____   _____   _____

_____   _____   _____   _____

2. Choose 4 words. Put each word into a sentence.

1. _____

2. _____

3. _____

4. _____

Note: Synonyms are words **meaning the same thing**: big, huge, large, enormous. A Thesaurus is a dictionary full of synonyms.

ed and ing

We can add **ed** and **ing** to verbs to make new words.

I jump.   I am jump**ing**.   I jump**ed**.

Complete the boxes by following the rules.

1. For some words, just add **ed** and **ing** to make new words.

play	played	playing
crack		
look		
fish		
kick		
cook		
mend		

2. After a single vowel and a single consonant double the last letter and add **ed** and **ing**.

shop	shopped	shopping
trip		
hop		
clap		
chop		
chat		
rub		

3. When a word ends in magic 'e', drop the 'e' and add **ed** and **ing**.

like	liked	liking
hope		
love		
save		
blame		
dine		
smile		

ck and short vowels

a e i o u   are vowels.

We put **'ck'** after a **short vowel** to make the **'k'** sound.

The short vowels are

a as in apple

e as in egg

u as in umbrella

i as in igloo

o as in octopus

Put a line under the short vowels in the words below. Sort the words. The first one is done for you.

crack   beck

luck

b_ack

s_ack
b_ack   chick   sick   deck

n_eck

fleck   shock

br_ick

pack   lock

tuck

black

cl_ock

stock   block

Jack

suck

thick   d_uck

pick

truck

speck

lick   peck   rock

stuck

Read the words.

Magic 'e' and long vowels

a e i o u are vowels.

We have **long vowels** in words which end in magic **'e'** (also called silent **'e'** or lazy **'e'**).

The long vowels are

a as in cake

e as in me

i as in bike

o as in smoke

u as in cube

Put a line under the **long vowels** in the words below.
Sort the words. The first one is done for you.

fire   hope

note   lake

~~made~~   fine

like   tape

c<u>a</u>ke

m<u>a</u>de

make

poke

game

coke

home

b<u>i</u>ke

slide   date

wine

slope   take

came

bite   rode

sm<u>o</u>ke

ride

Read the words.

Name _____ Date _____

Assimilation

'm' and 'n' are sounds we make down our noses.
They are difficult to hear.
Sometimes they 'get lost' in a word.

Listen for the **'m'** in lamp and the **'n'** in sand.

1. Read the words
   (listen for the **'m'**).

   Read the words
   (listen for the **'n'**).

lamp	and	lunch
damp	hand	bunch
camp	stand	munch
jump	end	punch
pump	mend	pinch
stamp	went	crunch
empty	tent	bench

2. Cover the word lists. See how many words you can remember. Write them.

_____

_____

_____

3. Put one of these **mp, nd, nt,** or **nch** words into each sentence.

   1. I can _____ into the pool.
   2. I can _____ on one leg.
   3. We can _____ in a _____.
   4. I sent a letter with a _____ on it.
   5. I can eat my packed _____.
   6. I had a _____ of flowers.
   7. I _____ to see my friend.

Name _____ Date _____

Wordsearch 1

Learn to spell like this:

Look   Say   Cover   Write   Check

1. Here are some words to spell.
   Read the words. Spell the words.

went   have   said   was

_____   _____   _____   _____

after   with   little   very

_____   _____   _____   _____

are   give   come   want

_____   _____   _____   _____

2. Find the words in the wordsearch. All the words go across. ——⟶
   Put a ring round the word when you find it.
   Cross the words off as you go along.

went   with
        little
have   very
        after
was   come
        said
are   give
        want

a	c	a	r	e	o	w	i	t	h	e
r	p	w	w	e	n	t	o	n	c	e
c	g	i	v	e	w	w	a	n	t	i
w	l	i	t	l	e	a	f	t	e	r
g	h	a	v	e	a	w	a	h	t	n
m	t	o	n	w	l	i	t	t	l	e
s	h	s	a	i	d	w	g	i	v	w
a	w	e	c	o	m	e	g	n	a	r
a	w	v	e	r	y	o	w	a	s	r

3. Which 4 words begin with 'w'?

_____

Which 2 words have 3 letters?

_____

Which word has 5 letters?

_____

Homophones 1

These 3 words sound the same, but they are spelt differently, and mean different things.

| to | I am going <u>to</u> swim. | I go <u>to</u> the shops. |

| two | I have <u>two</u> hands and <u>two</u> feet. |

| too | My dog came <u>too</u>. | My cat is <u>too</u> fat. |

1. Choose the right word. **to, two, too**

   1. I went _____ see my grandmother.

   2. I have _____ eyes.

   3. The elephant was _____ big to get in.

   4. I ran _____ school.

   5. I have _____ ears.

   6. My sister came _____ .

2. Write sentences using **to, two, too.**

   1. _____

   2. _____

   3. _____

   4. _____

Name _____   Date _____

Spell OW words

1. Find the correct word for each picture.
   Write the word under the picture.

owl

towel

crown

flower

tower

cow

clown

shower

2. Look for these **OW** words in the word worms. The first one is done for you.

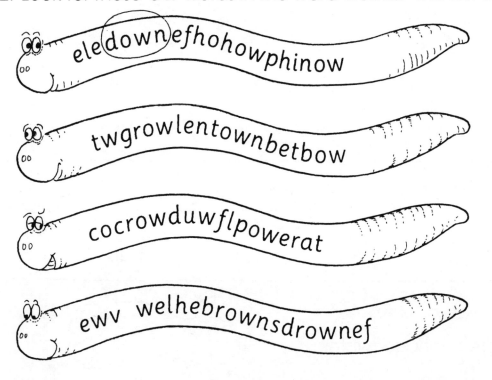

eledownefhohowphinow

twgrowlentownbetbow

cocrowduwflpowerat

ewv welhebrownsdrownef

down
crowd
growl
power
brown
how
drown
bow
vowel
now
town

Name _____   Date _____

Alliteration

Alliteration means that words which are near together start with the same sound.

Poems have alliteration.

Tongue-twisters have alliteration.

she sells sea shells on the
              sea shore.

1. Write a list of the animals using alliteration like this:

| 1 | | one white whale waiting, |
| one | | two ... |

      2
    two

3
three

      4
    four

5
five

      6
    six

7
seven

      8
    eight

9
nine

      10
    ten

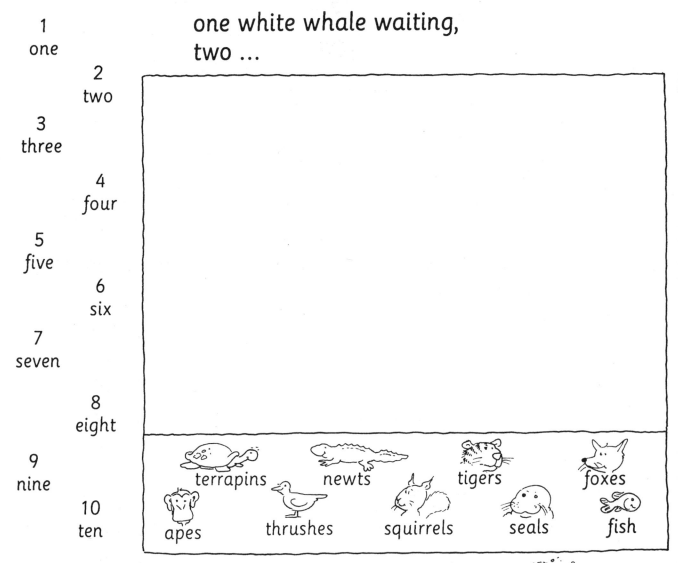

terrapins   newts   tigers   foxes

apes   thrushes   squirrels   seals   fish

2. Turn over and write a tongue-twister.

Name _____ Date _____

Spell **wh** words

There are 6 important question words which begin with '**wh**'. Read the words.

when where which why who what

Spell them this way:

Look	Say	Cover	Write	Check

_____ _____ _____ _____ _____

1. Some other words begin with 'wh'.
   Put the right word under the right picture. Read the words.

whisk

whistle

wheel

whisper

whale

wheat

whip

  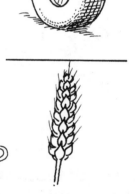

2. Put these words into sentences.

white _____

whiskers _____

while _____

wheel chair _____

whole _____

Spell le words

1. Find the correct word for each picture.

apple

angle

puzzle

handle

bicycle

jungle

circle

ankle

candle

bubble

stable

castle

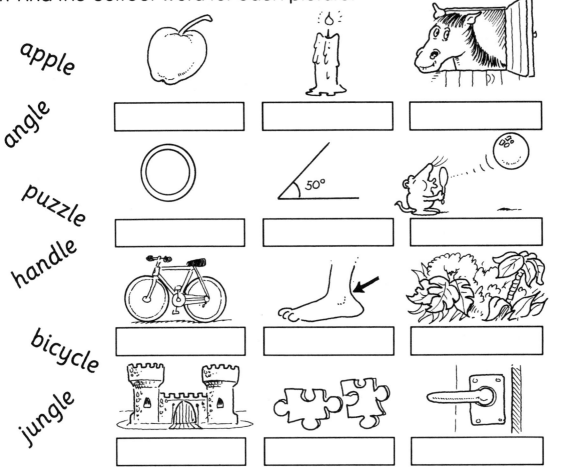

2. Look for these **le** words in the worms.
The first one is done for you.

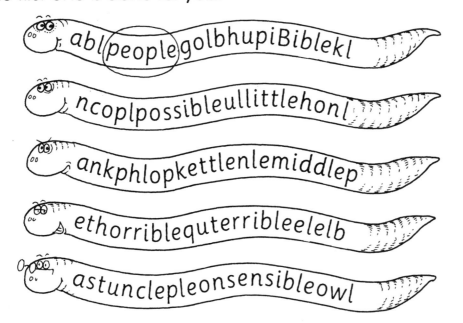

~~people~~
little
uncle
kettle
horrible
sensible
middle
Bible
possible
terrible

FOLENS SPELLING - Basic Rules Book 2 F3906 © Folens.

Know one - know lots!

Look at this word **old**.

When you know **old**, you can also spell:

bold, cold, fold, sold, told, gold, hold.

You can also make:

colder, golden, folded, holding, boldly, retold

by adding different beginnings or endings.

Add some beginnings or endings to these words to make new words. See how many you can make!

and

ill

ice

all

ink

arm

Name _____   Date _____

Alphabetical order

a b c d e f g h i j k l m n o p q r s t u v w x y z

1. Write the words in alphabetical order on the lines below. This will make a jungle story. Cross the words off as you go along.

Jungle cold, pythons At make great roll vanish. X-ray then explorers noises. Workers breakfast, sideways, insects. utterly damp quickly young -lions- zebras. Kings hungry fight Overhead,

A Jungle Story

At

2. Now on your own, or with a friend, try to make up a story with words in alphabetical order.

It can be like the one above, or like this:

One day, <u>a</u> <u>b</u>rown mouse <u>c</u>ame ...

a) Turn over.
b) Write the alphabet across the page.
c) Write your story.
d) Decorate your story with patterns or pictures.

Name _____ Date _____

Spell **ar** words

The **car** bumped
into the **farm cart**.

1. Put a ring round all the **ar** words in this story.

There are 17 words to find.

> It was dark with a few stars. Mark and Charlie Parker
> started their car. It sparked first time. They drove hard
> as they wanted to get to the fruit market by morning.
> Turning a sharp corner in the darkness, they missed the
> road and charged into a farm cart. They got out and
> marched across the garden to tell the farmer.

2. Write all the **ar** words you have found.

_____

_____

_____

_____

_____

Read the words.

3. Find **arm** in all these words. Put a ring round arm in each word.

army	disarm	disarmament	charm
harm	harmful	unharmful	farm
farming	alarm	alarming	alarmed

Turn over and spell these words. Pick 5 'ar' words to put into 5 sentences.

Spell igh words

igh makes a long i sound.
The **knight** went to **fight** in the **night**.

1. Add **igh** to make new words. Read the words.

S _ _ _   h _ _ _

2. Add **ight** to make new words. Read the words.

n	_____	l	_____
r	_____	br	_____
m	_____	sl	_____
f	_____	fl	_____
s	_____	kn	_____
t	_____	fr	_____

3. Choose a word from the lists to put in the sentences.

1. We see the moon at _____.
2. I can switch on the _____.
3. We can turn left or _____.
4. The light was _____.
5. The plane began its _____.
6. The boy got a _____.

4. Read these words: **midnight, frighten, tonight, delighted**. Put each one in a sentence.

1. _____
2. _____
3. _____
4. _____

Name _____ Date_____

Spell **or** words

The **h**or**se** was in
a st**or**m.

1. Put a ring round all the **or** words in this story.
   There are 21 words to find.

Sporty Nora set forth in the morning after a
short breakfast of cornflakes. She wore her
shorts and tore round the corner in record
time. She ran for forty minutes or more! She
did more sport in the afternoon and scored
a goal for her team. She was the star
performer on Sports Day!

Write all the **or** words you have found.

_____

_____

_____

_____

2. Here are 12 **sports**.
   Sort them into the boxes according to whether you use a ball or not.

swimming
golf
judo
athletics
karate
tennis
rugby
fishing
cricket
basketball
soccer
boxing

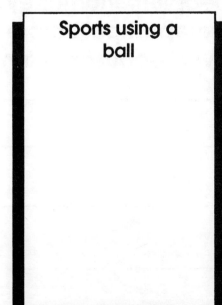

Sports using a ball	Sports not using a ball

Name _____   Date_____

Wordsearch 2

Here are some words to spell.

1. Read the words. Spell the words.

pull	push	over	under
_____	_____	_____	_____
water	use	ever	every
_____	_____	_____	_____
were	open	work	money
_____	_____	_____	_____
before	because	people	friend
_____	_____	_____	_____

2. All the same words are jumbled together in this box. Put a line where the words meet to divide them up. Write the words on the lines below. The first one is done for you.

every/waterworkopen
peoplefriendmoneyuse
werepushpullbefore
overbecauseeverunder

every _____ _____ _____

_____ _____ _____ _____

_____ _____ _____ _____

Homophones 2

These 3 words sound the same, but they are spelt differently, and mean different things.

'**there**' is about **place**.
It is over **there**.
There it is!

'**their**' is about **possession**.
Their friends came.
They had **their** bikes.

'**they're**' is short for **they are**.

They're very big fish
and **they're** good to eat.

1. Choose the right word: there, their, they're

   1. The ball is over_____.

   2. The spacemen went on _____mission.

   3. _____ the best runners in the class.

   4. The children ate _____ pizzas.

   5. We looked here and _____.

   6. _____ very good at dancing.

2. Write some sentences using **there**, **their**, **they're**.

_____

_____

_____

_____

Spell 'the' words

There are quite a lot of words beginning with **the**, or with **the** in them.

Look at these words. Read them.

the   theatre   bather   brother   thither   them

there   bother   tether   themselves

their   they   other   mother   father   another

weather   thermometer   then   whether

Sort out the words into 2 boxes.
(Cross the words off as you go along.)

Words with **the** in	Words beginning with **the**

Turn over and choose 5 'the' words to put into 5 sentences.

FOLENS SPELLING - Basic Rules Book 2 F3906   © Folens.

Name _____ Date _____

Syllables

A syllable is a group of letters said together.
A syllable can be one short word, or part of a longer word.

let = one syllable

let/ter = 2 syllables

let/ter/box = 3 syllables

Each syllable must have one vowel or more in it.

The vowels are a e i o u.

y can also be a vowel - often in the end syllable.

1. Read the words below. Sort the words into the 3 boxes. See if they have
   1, 2 or 3 syllables.
   The first one is done for you.

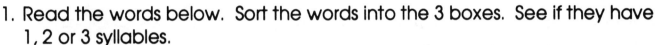

shopkeeper   big
someone
together   red   jam
                      goldfish   caravan
sun   dog   outside
windmill   cat   bluebell   happy
     bat   understand
animal   yesterday   Sunday   holiday

1 syllable words
sun

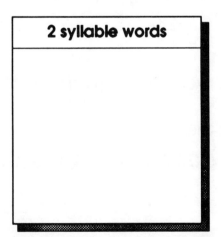

2 syllable words

3 syllable words

2. Turn over, draw 3 boxes and label them **1, 2** and **3**.
   Look in a book. Find 6 words with 1 syllable, 6 words with 2 syllables, and
   6 words with 3 syllables. Put them into boxes **1, 2** and **3** according to
   how many syllables there are in the words.

Name _____   Date_____

Y does 3 jobs

1. Read these words:
You can hear the sound **y** makes at the beginning of a word.

yacht

yo-yo

Read the words, spell the words without looking.

yes you your yet year yellow

_____

_____

2. When **y** is by itself at the end of a little word, it is like a vowel and makes a long **i** sound.

fly

Read the words. Spell the words without looking.

my by cry dry try fry fly spy shy

_____

_____

3. At the end of a longer word, y makes a short **i** sound.

sunny

Read the words. Spell the words without looking.

mummy daddy funny sunny happy

_____

_____

Turn over and put these 5 words into 5 sentences.

Spell ea words

Sometimes **ea** sounds like **ee**.
Here are some useful **ea** words.

1. Read the words. Spell the words without looking.

leaves 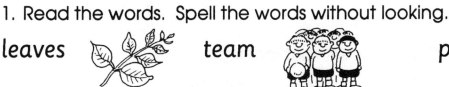	team	please
_____	_____	_____
read	steam	sea
_____	_____	_____
tea	east	seat
_____	_____	_____

2. Put 3 **ea** words together in one sentence.

beast   least   feast

The beast ate the least at the feast.

heat	meat	eat
beach	each	peach
steal	meal	real
team	dream	ice-cream

3. Here are some more **ea** words.
   Read the words. Spell the words without looking.

lead	clean	beam	deal
_____	_____	_____	_____
reach	stream	squeal	teacher
_____	_____	_____	_____
speak	cheap	easy	mean
_____	_____	_____	_____

Spell **tch** words

tch makes a **ch** sound after a short vowel. **tch** comes in the middle or at the end of a word.

Here are some useful **tch** words.

1. Read the words. Spell the words without looking.

match _____ watch _____ patch _____

catch _____ witch _____ kitchen _____

2. Put 2 tch words together in one sentence.

   fetch   watch

I   fetch   my watch   from the shop _____

match   pitch   _____

kitchen   ketchup   _____

twitch   itch   _____

witch   snatch   _____

3. Put a ring round **tch** in the words below.

   itch   stitch   hitch   hitchhiker

   matchbox   pitchfork   switch

   hotchpotch   hutch   crutch

Read the words. Turn over and spell these words. Choose 5 'tch' words to put into 5 sentences.

Spell OU words

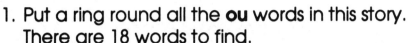

ou never comes at the end of a word.
ou often comes before d, t, th, nt and nd.

1. Put a ring round all the **ou** words in this story.
   There are 18 words to find.

The day was cloudy.
The hour was late.
A stout mouse, proudly
wearing loud trousers,
came out of his house.
He looked around - there
wasn't a sound, so he
bounded out across the
ground. He went to the
bank to put the round
pound he had found,
in his account.

2. Write all the **ou** words you have found. **Read the words.**

_____

_____

3. Add **ound** to these letters to make new words.
   Read the words.

f _____   w _____

p _____   r _____

s _____   ar _____

m _____   gr _____

h _____   b _____

4. Here are some more **ou** words to spell. Turn over and put these 6 'ou'
   words into 6 sentences.

   our, flour, count, shout, mouth, south

Spell **er** words

This is the most common spelling for the **er** sound.

1. Put a ring round all the **er** words in this story.
   There are 19 words to find.

   They were meeting to plan the term's winter fair - to be held in December. It was going to be bigger than ever! The teachers met the mothers and fathers to plan the number of stalls. They were going to put up silver streamers all over the hall. Letters were sent out, and everyone was going to bring brothers and sisters.

2. Write all the **er** words you have found.

   _____

   _____

   _____

   _____

3. The names of **jobs** which people do, sometimes end in **er**.

   'The **butcher**, the **baker**, the **candlestick** maker.'

   Write down as many jobs as you can, which end in **er**.

   _____

   _____

   _____

   _____

Name _____ Date_____

 # Spell **OA** words

oa   makes a long **o** sound, and is usually in the middle of words.

1. Put a ring round all the oa words in this story.
   There are 12 words to find.

   Joan got in a boat and it floated
   across the moat. Then a coach
   went along the road to the coast,
   but Joan moaned and groaned
   because a goat had eaten her
   coat.

2. Write all the **oa** words you have found.

   _____

   _____

   _____

3. Add **oat** to these letters to make   Add **oal** to these letters to make
   new words.   new words.

   b _____   g _____

   c _____

   m _____   f _____

   g _____   c _____

   fl _____

   thr _____   sh _____

Read the words.

4. Here are some more **oa** words to spell. Turn over and put these 5 'oa'
   words into 5 sentences.

         toad   *loaf*   *soap*   *cloak*   *soak*

Know one - know lots!

mark

re**mark**

market

marking

re**mark**ed

marker

land**mark**

re**mark**able

birth**mark**

You can make new words by adding different beginnings and endings.

Add beginnings and endings to these words to make new words.

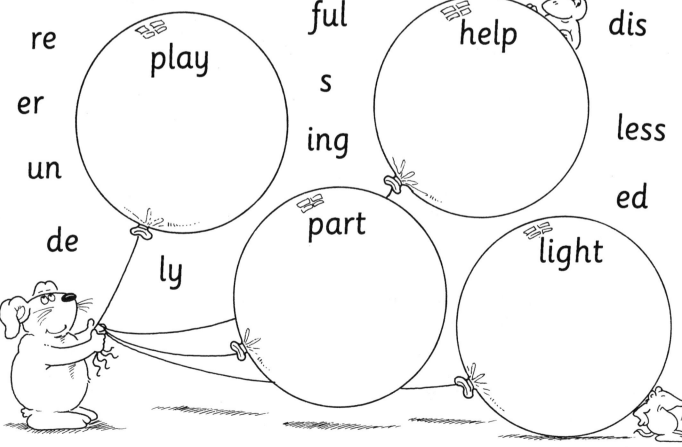

re
er
un
de

play

ly

ful
s
ing

part

help

light

dis
less
ed

FOLENS SPELLING - Basic Rules Book 2 F3906 © Folens.

Name _____   Date_____

ai and ay

ai and **ay** make a long **a** sound.
ai is usually at the beginning or middle of a word, and **ay** is usually at the end of a word.

We m**ay** have a w**ait**
for the tr**ain** tod**ay**.

1. Read the words. Spell the words without looking.

rain	_____	day	_____
train	_____	today	_____
brain	_____	stay	_____
pain	_____	May	_____
plain	_____	play	_____
paid	_____	way	_____
gain	_____	away	_____
again	_____	always	_____

2. Put one of these **ai** or **ay** words into the sentences.

    play   away   train   rain

   1. Look at the clouds - it may_____.

   2. I'm going out to_____.

   3. We went to catch the_____.

   4. My kite blew_____.

3. All the days of the week end in ay.
    Write them in order.

_____   _____   _____

_____   _____   _____   _____

4. Turn over and check you can spell all the 12 months of the year as well!

Spell **dge** words

No word in English (except Raj) ends in **j**.
The **j** sound in the middle or at the end off words can be **ge** or **dge**.
The **dge** letter string always follows a short vowel.

1. Read this limerick.
   Put a ring round the **dge** words.
   There are 9 words to find.

A podgy young lodger from Cambridge,
Was stung, on a bridge, by a tame midge.
Then up trudged a judge,
Who fed it some fudge,
And was stung, near a hedge, by the same midge!

2. Write all the **dge** words you have found.

   _____

   _____

   _____

   _____

3. Look for these **dge** words in the word worms.
   The first one is done for you.

edge
badge
hedge
bridge
ridge
badger
ledge
budgie

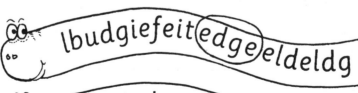

lbudgiefeit(edge)eldeldg

brioledgeoiebadgeldleg

gerthedgemdgeridgeae

eabridgeledgibadgeroe

oi and oy

oi is usually at the beginning or middle of words. **oy** is usually at the end of words.

Jo**y**'s n**oi**sy t**oy**
ann**oy**ed the b**oy**s.

1. Read the words. Spell the words.

coin	_____	roy	_____
oil	_____	boy	_____
boil	_____	toy	_____
join	_____	joy	_____
joint	_____	enjoy	_____
point	_____	cowboy	_____
voice	_____	destroy	_____
noise	_____	employ	_____

2. Put one of these oi or oy words into each sentence.

oink! oink! oink!

1. My pencil has a sharp_____.
2. The boy dressed up as a_____.
3. The pigs made a lot of _____.
4. The wolf spoke in a soft _____.
5. I _____ playing with my _____.
6. A car engine needs _____.

3. Put a ring round **oi** and **oy** in the words below.

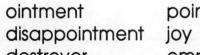

ointment	point	appoint	disappoint
disappointment	joy	enjoy	enjoyment
destroyer	employ	employment	

Read the words. Turn over and spell these words. Choose 5 of these `oi' and `**oy**' words to put into 5 sentences.

Name _____ Date _____

Wordsearch 3

Look at this word - **once**.
It is hidden in this sentence:

Don't put salt **on ce**lery!

1. There are 7 words hidden in the sentences below. Find the words.
   Put a ring round each word, and write the word at the end of the
   sentence.
   The first one is done for you.

They	please	many	your	who	other	down

1. **The y**ellow book is mine.   _They_____

2. Are you really going away?   _____

3. Where is the man you saw?   _____

4. I want an apple as everyone does.   _____

5. Open the window near you.   _____

6. It's on the left and also the right.   _____

7. The cow hopped away.   _____

2. Hide these 4 words in sentences for your friends to find.

made _____

into _____

them _____

some _____

Name _____ Date_____

Homophones 3

Homophones are words which sound the same, but they are spelt differently and they mean different things.

I **won** the race.  I have **one** mouth.

1. There are pairs of homophones below. **One word** in each pair has been put into a sentence. Put the **other word** into a sentence to show you know what it means.

by	I sat by my friend.
buy	_____
meet	I ran to meet my Gran.
meat	_____
our	This is our school.
hour	_____
right	This is my right hand.
write	_____
new	My bag is new.
knew	_____
here	Here is the right shop.
hear	_____

2. Turn over and make a list of homophones and put pictures by the side to help you remember which word is which. Here are some to start you off: see sea, rode road, wear where, for four, paw poor.

Spell **ur** words

ur sounds like **er**.

The n**ur**se took a p**ur**se
to ch**ur**ch on Th**ur**sday.

1. Here are some useful **ur** words. Read the words. Spell the words.
   (Don't forget to Look - Say - Cover - Write - Check.)

turn	burn	return	burnt
_____	_____	_____	_____
hurt	church	surprise	fur
_____	_____	_____	_____
Thursday	Saturday		curtain
_____	_____		_____

2. Put one of these **ur** words into each sentence.
   1. I go to school on _____.
   2. I don't go to school on _____.
   3. Look at the bonfire_____!
   4. When I go to bed, I draw my_____.
   5. Now it's my _____ to have a go!
   6. Some people go to _____ on Sunday.

3. Put a ring round **ur** in the words below.

spurs	burst	bursting	murder
furry	further	furthermore	surprising
turkey	curl	curly	murmur

Read the words. Turn over and spell these words. Choose 5 'ur' words to
put into 5 sentences.

Note - **ur** is a more common spelling than **ir**.

Name _____ Date_____

Spell **ir** words

ir sounds like **er**.

Thirteen dirty birds in a
fir tree.

1. Here are some useful **ir** words. Read the words. Spell the words.
   (Don't forget to Look - Say - Cover - Write - Check.)

fir	firm	first	dirty	sir
_____	_____	_____	_____	_____

bird	birth	birthday	shirt
_____	_____	_____	_____

skirt	thirteen	thirty	girl
_____	_____	_____	_____

2. Put one of these **ir** words into each sentence.

   1. Each year I have a_____.

   2. 3 x 10 = _____.

   3. I was_____ in the race!

   4. The _____ went out on her bike.

   5. My boots were _____.

3. Put a ring round **ir** in the words below.

stir	stirring	third	thirsty	squirt

squirting	infirmary	firstly	squirm

Read the words. Turn over and spell these words. Choose 5 'ir' words to
put into 5 sentences.

Note - ir is found in the numbers **thir**teen and **thir**ty.

Name _____   Date_____

Letter patterns on number plates

Sometimes you can make words up from car number plates, by adding other letters. **Keep the letters in the same order.**

stunned   **stand**

seated   **Saturday**

insisted   **standard**

strained   **assisted**

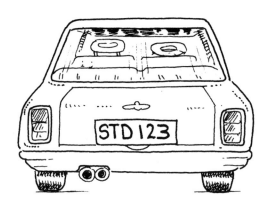

On your own, or with a friend, see how many words you can make from these number plates.

Keep the letters in the same order.

ARK 46   _____

_____

SON 32   _____

_____

DNL 81   _____

_____

PTR 11   _____

_____

BTF 57   _____

_____

Now make up some number plates for your friends to try.

  **Soft c**

'c' **always** says 's' when it is followed by **e** **i** or **y**.

cell

cinema

cycle

1. Here are some useful **soft c** words. Read the words. Spell the words.
   (Don't forget to Look - Say - Cover - Write - Check.)

cell	centre	ice	mice	nice
_____	_____	_____	_____	_____

space	prince	princess	city
_____	_____	_____	_____

circle	circus	cinema	pencil
_____	_____	_____	_____

2. Choose 6 words. Put each word into a sentence.

1. _____
2. _____
3. _____
4. _____
5. _____
6. _____

3. Put a ring round all the **soft c** elements in the words below (ce, ci, cy).
   Read the words.

decide	decided	deciding	decision
bicycle	tricycle	fancy	fanciful
race	twice	rice	face

Turn over and spell these words. Choose 5 **soft c** words to put into 5
sentences.

Soft g

'g' **sometimes** says 'j' when it is followed by **e** **i** or **y.**

gem   gingerbread man   gypsy

1. Here are some useful **soft g** words. Read the words. Spell the words.
   (Don't forget to Look - Say - Cover - Write - Check.)

   gem   gentle   gentleman

   _____   _____   _____

   orange   danger   age   page

   _____   _____   _____   _____

   cage   strange   magic

   _____   _____   _____

2. Choose 6 words. Put each word into a sentence.

   1. _____
   2. _____
   3. _____
   4. _____
   5. _____
   6. _____

3. Put a ring round all the **soft g** elements in these words (ge, gi, gy). Read
   the words.

   change   manage   engine   engineer   stranger

   large   giant   magician   Egypt   village

Turn over and spell these words. Pick 5 **soft g** words to put into 5 sentences.

Name _____   Date _____

Mnemonics

Some words are tricky to spell.
A **mnemonic** or trick can help you.

1. Here are some **mnemonics** that have been made up, to help with
   difficult words.

island

Yes - it **is land**!

(a) _____

(b) Think of a picture: L ôôk   ēyēs

(c) Say the word in a silly way:
   say **was** like **has**.
   say the silent **k** in **knock**.
   say the **c** in **scissors**.

(d) To remember | **ight** |, say 'I go home tonight.'

(e) To remember **could**, **would** and **should**.
   say: 'Oh **you** little **d**arling' - (o, u, l, d).

2. Often, the first letter of each word in a sentence
   can give you the spelling.
   '**S**even **a**nts **i**n **d**anger' = 'said'.

   Work out the words from these mnemonics:

   Better eat caramels at uncle's special event= _____

   Poor little elephants and six eggs = _____

   A nice sweet with extra raspberries = _____

   Do octopuses eat sweets = _____

3. Feel **blue** on **Tue**sday. See your **fri**end on **Fri**day.

4. Turn over and make up mnemonics for words **you** find hard to spell.

Name _____   Date _____

 # Silent l and silent k

Silent l   'l' is silent in some words.
Follow the lines to find the word pairs.
Write the words in pairs on the lines. Read them.

could   yolk   walk

half   palm   chalk

calf   folk   stalk

talk   calm   would

1/2 = half

_____ _____

_____ _____

_____ _____

_____ _____

_____ _____

_____ _____

Silent k   'k' is always silent with 'n'.
Here are some useful **kn** words.
Read them. Spell them without looking.

knot	knee	kneel	knock
knit	knitting	knife	knight
know	knowing	knowledge	knew

Look up the meaning of these words in a dictionary. Write the meanings next to the words.

knapsack _____

knead _____

knoll _____

knuckle _____

to knuckle down _____

Silent b and silent w

Silent b   'b' is silent in some words (often with 'm').
Follow the lines to find the word pairs.
Write the words in pairs on the lines. Read them.

bomb   comb   lamb   climber

thumb   climb   crumb

_____ _____

_____ _____

_____ _____

_____ _____

lambs   bombs   climber   _____ _____

combs   thumbs   crumbs   _____ _____

Silent w   'w' is always silent with 'r'.
Here are some useful **wr** words.
Read them. Spell them without looking.

write   writer   writing   written
_____   _____   _____   _____
wrote   wrap   wrapping   wrong

_____   _____   _____   _____
wren   wreck   wrestle   wrestling

_____   _____   _____   _____

Write the names of your favourite writers here:

_____

_____

'b' is silent with 't'. Look up the meaning of these words in a dictionary:
doubt, debt, subtle. Turn over and write the words and their meanings.

Name _____ Date_____

Prefixes un_ re_

Pre means 'before'.

A prefix is a letter or group of letters put at the beginning of a word to change its meaning. You do not change the spelling of a word when you add a prefix to it.

1. **un** means 'not'.
   Put **un** in front of these words to make new words.
   Write the new words in the body.

tie	do	lock	just	safe
kind	pack	happy	lucky	
usual	pleasant	easy		

   * Read the new words. *

   unhappy

2. **re** means 'again'.

   Put **re** in front of these words to make new words.
   Write the new words in the bottle.

   refill

tell	place	name	wind
new	move	plant	cycle
call	fresh	port	discover

   * Read the new words. *

3. Turn over and draw 3 boxes (about 5cm x 10cm).
   Label the boxes with the prefixes: **con, ex, dis.**

   ('**con**' means 'together' or 'with'. '**ex**' means 'out of' or the opposite of 'in'. '**dis**' means 'not' or 'away'.)
   Put words into the boxes that begin with the 3 prefixes. Use a dictionary to help you.

FOLENS SPELLING - Basic Rules Book 2 F3906   © Folens.

Name _____ Date _____

Suffixes -tion -ous -ture
(word endings) ('shun') ('us') ('cher')

A suffix is a letter or group of letters put at the end of a word to change the way you use the word (-**ing**, **ed**, **er** are common suffixes).

Read the words below.
Look at the **suffixes** and sort the words into the right boxes according to their suffixes.

(Cross them out as you go along.)

joyous   picture   dangerous   station   action

famous   mixture   furniture   jealous   marvellous

question   tremendous

future   capture   information   adventure

enormous   manufacture   mention   conversation   attention

tion	ous	ture

Turn over and draw 2 boxes.
Label them with the suffixes - **ment**, **ness**.
Put as many words as you can in each box, that end with the 2 suffixes.
Here are some to start you off: move**ment**, dark**ness**, good**ness**, depart**ment**, bold**ness**.

Diagnostic dictations

Here are two dictation passages. Dictation 1 is suitable for children aged 7-8 years, and Dictation 2 for children aged 8-9 years. The passages can be given to individual children, to a group, or to a class. The passages each contain 100 words, so a percentage score may be obtained. An **analysis** of the types of errors made will be of far more value than the score achieved, however.

Dictate the passage slowly and clearly in small phrases, indicating where punctuation marks should be. Encourage children to 'have a go' with every word.

1. One day, a boy called Lee went to see his friend Kim who lived in a big block of flats. He had to climb a lot of steps to reach the top floor where she lived. Kim's mother gave them some food as they were going out on their bikes. Soon they had put on their coats, said goodbye, and set off down the road. They had planned to go to the park. Then there was a crash of thunder and some small spots of rain. Kim swung off the road and rested under a tree, and Lee came too.

2. One bright holiday morning, I was looking forward to a wonderful spring treat. I had saved some money to get a new pet. I wasn't quite sure what animal to get, a furry hamster or a striped snake! I remembered to call for Vicky and together we went, full of excitement. But I had forgotten it was Thursday and the shops were closed!

    In dejection we returned home to discover that my thoughtful, generous grandma had bought me a perfect little mouse, as a present she said. I was really thrilled with the welcome gift, and quickly named it 'Squeak'.

Classification of errors

Once the dictation passages have been collected and marked, the errors - or miscues - can be classified. This classification derives from Peters' work and Torbe's work (see Appendix). A classification gives indication as to follow-up work.

The more reasonable alternatives there are, the better the spelling; the more unclassifiable errors there are, the worse the spelling. Look for the **bit** of the word that is wrong, and this will indicate the letter strings or word families to be learnt.

1. **Reasonable errors.**
    Reasonable errors ('clime' for 'climb' or 'treet' for 'treat') show that the child is applying phonic rules, and a little 'fine tuning' is needed to rectify these errors.

2. **Auditory errors**
    Auditory errors may indicate problems with hearing or articulation, or the child may be failing to write down the correct letters for sounds heard. There may be problems with consonants (v/f/th confusion), blends ('b' for 'bl'), vowels (i/e confusion) or syllable difficulties ('hast' for 'hamster').

3. **Word ending errors**
    There may be errors with 'ful', 'tion', 'ed', 'ing', 'ly' or 'ous'. This will suggest which letter strings need follow-up activities.

4. **'Irregularly spelt' words**
    Irregularly spelt words such as 'who', 'said', 'sure', or 'they' may cause trouble to a number of children. These spellings may then be put into personal wordbooks, taken home to practise, or displayed on a class wall chart.

5. **Unclassifiable errors.**
    A large number of unclassifiable errors such as 'ricer' for 'reach' , or 'gathe' for 'returned', means that a basic spelling programme needs to be drawn up for a particular child. It may also be advisable to call in specialist help.

Poor **handwriting** may be a mask for poor spelling, and correct letter formation and joining practice may be needed. This should be noted on the record sheet (see over).

Correction of spelling errors, or miscues, should lead to new learning. Children need their attention drawn to the bit of the word that is wrong, and they need to become increasingly aware of the likely letter combinations in English.

Diagnostic spelling record sheet   Sheet No

Name_____ Date_____ Age_____ Class_____ Year_____

1. Reasonable errors	2. Auditory errors	3. Word ending errors	4. 'Irregularly spelt' words	5. Unclassifiable errors
e.g. 'flor' for 'floor'.	e.g. 'cash' for 'crash'.	e.g. 'pland' for 'planned'.	e.g. 'siad' for 'said'.	e.g. 'wact' for 'where'.

Suggestions for follow-up work:

FOLENS SPELLING - Basic Rules Book 2 F3906

Word list 1

100 most used words in English.

a
about
all
an
and
are
as
at
back
be
been
before
big
but
by
call
came
can
come
could
did
do
down
first
for
from
get
go
had
has
have
he
her
here
him
his
I
if
in
into
is
it
just
like

little
look
made
make
me
more
much
must
my
new
no
not
now
of
off
old
on
one
only
or
our
over
other
out
right
said
see
she
so
some
that
the
their
them
then
there
they
this
to
two
up
want
was
we

well
went
were
what
when
where
which
who
will
with
you
your

Other useful words.

after
again
along
almost
always
animal
another
any
around
ask
away
because
between
biscuit
bought
break
brought
brother
build
buy
children
climb
does
done
every
fast
father
friend
give
going
gone
great
guess

happy
island
know
last
live
love
many
morning
money
mother
move
nothing
once
open
people
please
police
pull
put
shall
should
sugar
sure
talk
thank
thought
through
use
usual
walk
water
while
why
wonderful
work
would
wrong
year
yet
young
yourself
zero

* Source:
McNally, J. and
Murray, W. - see
Appendix.

Word list 2

This list is based on the letter patterns or letter strings found in this book.

star
swan
plug
tree
slide
spider
snail
frog
broom
clock
drum
cross
grass
fly
glass
pram
blocks
smile

splash
screw
spring
string
square

looked
looking
shopped
shopping
liked
liking

sack
neck

brick
clock
duck

cake
game
bike
pine
smoke
rode

went
tent

lamp
camp
hand
mend
lunch
munch

owl
crown

wheel
whip

apple
candle

might
light
car
farm

for
horse

read
team

match
catch

out
cloud

her
teacher

boat
toad

rain
train

day
play

happy
sunny

edge
badge

oil
point

boy
enjoy

turn
church

first
bird

cell
cycle

gem
gentle

half
calf

knot
knee

lamb
climb

write
wrap

undo
untie

recall
replace

action
station

picture
future

joyous
enormous

Family words: mother, mum, father, dad, sister, brother, grandmother, grandfather, aunt, uncle, baby.

Planet names: Mercury, Venus, Earth, Mars, Jupiter, Saturn, Uranus, Neptune, Pluto.

Numbers, one to ten. Animal names. Occupations. Days of the week. Months of the year.

Appendix

Books, Spelling Programmes, Workbooks, Computer Programs.

Books

1. Bissex G.L. (1980) *Gnys at Wrk*. Harvard University Press.
2. Bryant, P.E. and Bradley, L. (1985) *Children's Reading Problems*. Blackwell.
3. Daniels, J.C. and Diack, H. (1979) *The Standard Reading Tests*. Hart-Davis.
4. Dictionaries: *A.C.E.* (Aurally Coded English), L.D.A.
   Pergamon Dictionary of Perfect Spelling. Pergamon.
   Both these dictionaries are for children who experience difficulties with spelling. Words can be found according to their sound - e.g. 'psychology' can be found under 'p' and under 's'.
5. Gentry, J.R. (1987) *Spel .... is a Four Letter Word*. Scholastic.
6. Hornsby, B. and Shear, F. (1976) *Alpha to Omega*. Heinemann.
7. McNally, J. and Murray, W. (1970) *Key Words to Literacy*. The Teacher Publishing Company, Northants.
8. National Curriculum Documents (1989) *English in the National Curriculum*. H.M.S.O.
9. Peters, M.L. (1975) *Diagnostic and Remedial Spelling Manual*. Macmillan.
10. Schonell, F.J. (1976) *Graded Word Spelling Test*. L.D.A.
11. Thesauri: *Junior Thesaurus*. Collins
    The Young People's Thesaurus Dictionary. Ward Lock Ed.
12. Torbe, M. (1977) *Teaching Spelling*. Ward Lock Ed.
13. Vernon, P.E. (1977) *Spelling Test*. N.F.E.R./Nelson.
14. Vincent, D. and Claydon, J. (1982) *Diagnostic Spelling Test*. N.F.E.R./Nelson.

Spelling programmes/workbooks

1. *Attack Spelling Programme*. (100 systematically structured spelling lessons.) Richards, J.P.B.S. Nottingham.
2. *Catchwords - Ideas for Teaching Spelling*. (A set of six graded workbooks.) Cripps, C. (1978) Harcourt Brace Jovanvich.
3. *Spelling Made Easy*. Brand, V. Egon Publishers Ltd.
4. *Sounds, Pictures, Words*. (Graded workbooks for 5-8-year-olds.) Hughes, J. Nelson.
5. *Stile Spelling Programme*. (Self-correcting spelling programme for 5-14-year-olds.) L.D.A.

Spellchecker

Franklin Elementary Spellmaster (QES90). (Designed for children, with 26,800 words in it.) Innovations International Ltd., Richmond, Surrey.

Computer programs

Hands on Spelling. E.S.M. Cambs. (Training visual memory.)
Short Vowel Sounds. 'Magic E'. 'Consonant blends'. 'Vowel digraphs'. 'Word Builder'. Five programs to help children with phonics. Sherston Software, Malmesbury, Wilts.
Spelling Week by Week. Levels 1 and 2 are for children aged 7. Chalksoft Ltd., P.O.Box 49, Spalding.
Star Spell (for younger children) and *Star Spell Plus* (for older children).
Fisher Marriott, Lower Fulbrook, Warwick, CV35 8AS.